G000094502

THINGS
TO DO
ON THE
LOO

An exclusive edition for:

for all your gift books and gift stationery

Published in 2017 by Allsorted. Watford, Herts, U.K. WD19 4BG

ISBN: 978-1-910562-97-0

Written by Michael Powell
Illustrations reproduced courtesy of Shutterstock.com
Concept by Milestone Design
Designed by Joanna Ross at Double Fish Design Ltd

Printed in China

Every effort has been made to ensure the accuracy of the information contained in this book.
In the unlikely case of queries please contact the compilers via their website www.susannageoghegan.com.

INTRODUCTION

Did you know that women spend on average about 85 minutes a week on the toilet? Men spend even longer – about 105 minutes. That's between 2 and 2.5 working weeks a year, depending on your gender. Are you using that time wisely?

Here is a steaming pile of puzzles, conundrums, activities and aphorisms to confound, amuse and educate your brain tank. There are even 100 national flags for you to learn as well as the definitive guide to the use of apostrophes.

Dip into all the toilet based trivia: did you know, for example, that one per cent of people will accidentally drop this book into the bowl? Probably. Anyway, enjoy the ride and don't forget to wash your hands afterwards.

MAKE A TOILET ROLL
TUBE GIFT
BOX

Nothing says 'thank you' like a home-crafted gift box, a little gem of an idea that lets your nearest and dearest know how much you care about them.

YOU WILL NEED:
A toilet roll
Craft knife
Small strip of gift paper
String, ribbon, wool or raffia

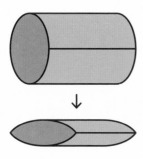

1. Lay a toilet roll flat on a work surface and press down on it so that it's flattened along its length.

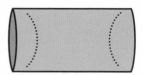

2. Using a craft knife, cut a semi-circle at each end of the toilet roll, making sure the cut goes through to the other side. Take care that your cuts start and finish just short of the very end of the roll.

3. Fold in the ends at the semi-circular cuts to form the edge of your box.

4. Paint the toilet roll tube gift box a bright colour and leave to dry.

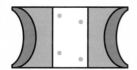

5. Decorate with a strip of gift paper wrapped around the centre of the box and secured with glue or tape.

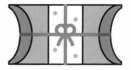

6. Finish the box with string, cord, wool, ribbon or raffia tied around the length of the box so that both ends are secured.

TOILET TRIVIA

The average tear is 5.90 sheets of toilet paper. 44 per cent wipe from front to back from behind their backs; 60 per cent look at the paper after they wipe; 42 per cent fold, 33 per cent crumple, 8 per cent both fold and crumple, 6 per cent wrap it around their hands. 2 per cent have wiped with money.

Forty per cent of water used in the home is flushed down the toilet. The average toilet is flushed eight times a day, using an average of five gallons per flush. About 75 per cent of the water we consume in our homes is used in the bathroom.

The French word 'toile' means cloth or net. When the French began covering their dressing tables with cloth, the tablecloth was also called a 'toile', and the dressing room was called a 'toilette'. When the first flushing apparatuses were invented, they were located in the dressing rooms and became known as toilets.

SLITHERLINK

Connect adjacent corners horizontally or vertically to
form a single closed path, with no extra branches.

Example

The path cannot cross itself.

A number tells you how many
lines surround that square.

THERE IS ONE UNIQUE SOLUTION.

Example grid:
```
3   1 2 3
  2 2 3   1
  2 2   1
1   1   1   1
    1   2 2
1   0 2 2
  1 1 1     3
```

Main puzzle grid:

	2		2		3	
2	2					2
3	2	2	2	3		2
2	2	3		1	0	1
1		1	1	1	0	1
0					1	1
	1		1		2	

THREE TOILETS

An elderly estate agent is selling an old town house which has three toilets, one on each of its three floors (ground, first, second). Each is lit by a single light bulb, all three switches are located in the entrance hall on the ground floor but they aren't labelled.

She wants to find out which switch operates which bulb but her angina means she can only climb one flight of stairs. All three switches are currently in the 'off' position. What should she do?

TAO OF THE TOILET

DIARRHOEA RELIEF

A visit to the bathroom is a daring adventure or nothing at all.

You cannot always control your situation, but you can control how you react to it.

My bowl overflows with happiness and love.

Today is rich with opportunities and I open myself to greet them.

I deserve whatever good passes through me today.

I courageously open myself and move every stream of opportunity.

I am in charge of my sphincter.

Today and every day I choose to give to the bowl.

The relief I seek is also seeking me.

I am thankful and blessed that I get to release these blind eels into the sea.

BATHROOM
ETIQUETTE
QUIZ

There are many unwritten rules with regard to using the bathroom, whether at home or in public spaces. What kind of bathroom user are you? Do you show due care and consideration for others while parking your breakfast or are you borderline feral?
Answer these five questions to find out.

1. At the office you walk into the only free cubicle to see a massive phantom log staring up at you from the bowl. It's so huge it probably generates its own weather system. What do you do?

A. Leave immediately. I can't risk someone thinking that I did that.
B. Flush several times until it disappears.
C. Do your business, flush and leave, regardless.
D. Make loud straining noises then stride proudly out of the cubicle and beckon to the next visitor (maybe even charge admission).

2. You've just finished your business and now it's time to wipe. Just then your boss walks into the next-door cubicle. What do you do?

A. Wait for them to leave before you begin.
B. Flush the toilet to mask the sound.
C. Wipe as quietly as possible.
D. Wipe away loudly and proudly, accompanied by satisfied grunts of admiration.

---

3. All the cubicles are busy and you are bursting. What do you do?

A. Wait patiently for one to become free.
B. Knock on the cubicle doors to see if one is free.
C. Look under the doors to check for legs.
D. Go in the sink because it's better than making a mess on the floor.

---

4. You're in the middle of an important mobile phone conversation when nature calls. What do you do?

A. Finish the call and then go to the bathroom.
B. End the call politely and call back after you've been to the bathroom.
C. Take them into the loo with you, but talk quietly (and don't flush).
D. Give them a blow-by-blow account of your progress.

---

5. How often do you wash your hands?

A. Every time I use the bathroom, without fail.
B. Always, unless I'm in a hurry.
C. Only when other people are watching.
D. Never.

THE RESULTS

MOSTLY As:

You are a fastidious and considerate bathroom user who always puts everyone else's needs before your own. You may be overly concerned about what others think of you, which makes you backward in coming forward and you could benefit from being more assertive at times. For example, when you're touching cloth, it's no time to rigorously observe the social niceties. Try not to invest all your energy into doing what you think others want, otherwise one day you'll get bitten by your own corndogs.

MOSTLY Bs:
You're assertive, practical and willing to get stuck in for the general good. You're a realist who isn't afraid to metaphorically and literally take a dump in the woods when matters are pressing. However, you also possess a healthy degree of discretion and avoid advertising your intestinal wares. You set achievable boundaries, but when you're caught short you yield to the natural imperative of dropping a wad rather than slavishly adhering to cultural norms.

MOSTLY Cs:
You like to think you're an egestive maverick, a loan wolf who squeezes one out and then quietly disappears into the night. But you mustn't overlook the protection and comfort offered by the pack. No person is an island, we all have to observe certain standards to reduce the risk of spreading social malaise and illness. It's time to wake up and realise that you aren't the pearl in the oyster, or even the grit.

MOSTLY Ds:
You're a high functioning sociopath, who is incapable of understanding the needs of others. You have a puerile fascination with bodily functions. Your exhibitionism and complete disregard for common decency single you out as either a political lobbyist or a reality television 'celebrity'. There's a 99 per cent probability you are male.

BATHROOM TILES

Look at these two rows of tiles on your bathroom floor. How many different rectangles can you make by drawing round these eight tiles (remember, a square is a type of rectangle)?

SIT AND PONDER

RIDDLE WHILE YOU PIDDLE

1 While holidaying alone in a remote stone cottage, you decide to take a long, hot soak in the tub. As you turn the tap, the handle comes away in your hand, sending a torrent of water pouring with force from the tap. Nothing you do succeeds in stopping the flow of water. The bathroom is windowless and soon the water spills out of the bath and starts filling up the bathroom. You try the door: it's wedged shut. There's no escape.

How do you save yourself from drowning?

 You're trekking in the mountains with a friend. You came prepared for one night under the stars, but towards the end of the second day, an extreme weather front descends upon you very fast and as night falls, you realise you need to do whatever you can to protect yourselves from the cold. You need to make a fire, urgently. Between you, you have just one match, along with some tightly wound twine, a candle and some toilet paper.

Which do you light first?

URINAL CAKE

A janitor is servicing eight urinals but only has one circular urinal cake. How can he cut the cake into eight equal pieces using only three straight cuts?

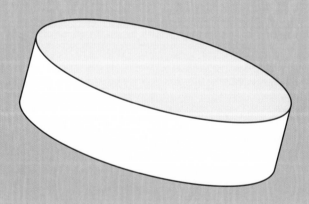

MOVE
TOILET ROLLS
WITH YOUR MIND

This trick requires two toilet roll tubes and a little bit of classic misdirection.

Place two toilet roll tubes side by side on a table with the open ends facing you.

Tell your audience that you can move toilet paper tubes with your mind. It's not the coolest of superpowers or the most useful, but it's still pretty impressive! Announce that you will make these toilet roll tubes repel each other and fly apart.

Now begin to channel your superpowers into the toilet roll tubes. Place your hands just above the tubes, with palms facing the table and with fingers closed. Start humming.

Spend a minute or so increasing the volume and resonance of your humming and to raise the anticipation of your star-struck spectators.

Build the hum to an impressive crescendo and then suddenly lower your head as you raise the pitch and force air through your closed lips to a point between the two tubes. Your humming should disguise the sound of the air rush.

The blast of air will send the tubes flying apart. Follow their movements with each hand to make it look as though you are moving them with the force of your will.

DRUG DILEMMA

Your doctor has prescribed you two separate bottles of pills. Every day you are supposed to take one pill from Bottle A and half a pill from Bottle B (snap it in half). You take out one pill from each bottle, but your phone rings and you get distracted. Five minutes later you look at the two identical pills and you can't remember which is which. You don't want to waste any medicine, so rather than throwing away the pills and starting again, how can you use these pills to take the correct dose?

THREE UTILITIES

3D PUZZLE

There are three toilets and three utilities: electricity plant, water source and sewerage plant. You must connect each toilet to all three utilities, using nine separate lines in total, but they must not cross and they cannot pass through toilets or utility buildings.
[Hint: you can only solve this by thinking in three dimensions rather than two. Also, think of a doughnut!]

MAKE A TOILET ROLL
TUBE CAT

YOU WILL NEED:
A number of toilet rolls, and/or
kitchen paper rolls
Paint
Sticky tape
Scissors

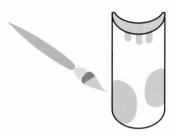

1. Fold down the top of a toilet roll tube to form the top of the head and ears.

2. Decide what colour you want your cat to be and paint the outside of the toilet roll and the inside of the bottom end (ginger, black and white, grey, etc.).

3. Paint a pink triangle for the inside of each ear. Leave to dry.

4. Cut a thin sliver of cardboard from around the bottom of the roll, but leave it attached.

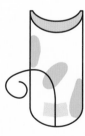

5. Tape the tail halfway up the body.

6. Copy a face onto the front of the toilet roll or make up your own.

TWO MORAL
BATHROOM
CONUNDRUMS
TALES FROM AN
UNDERGROUND BATHROOM

You're caught short while out in the city and head into an underground public toilet. It charges a fee to everyone who uses it, with a narrow turnstile gate at its entrance. You pay your money and take relief in a cubicle. But as you're washing your hands, a warning alarm begins to ring: there's a fire. Realising it's not a drill, everyone in the bathroom queues nervously at the turnstile to escape but blocking the way is a woman heavily pregnant with twins. She gets stuck and no amount of gentle manoeuvring is working her loose. As smoke billows down the stairway into the bathroom, you realise you have a choice. Either she stays where she is, and everyone risks asphyxiation, or else as a crowd, you manhandle the woman free, knowing that there is no way of doing so without causing her and her unborn babies significant injury.

What do you do?

CAUGHT SHORT AT WORK

You're a hard-working, dedicated but low-paid employee. You're the first in every day and the last to leave. You've not taken sick leave in forever, cut no corners and are everyone's favourite co-worker. But your pay is abysmal, and you spend the last week in every month with an empty wallet, living on meagre remnants from the darkest recesses of your refrigerator.

One morning, five penniless days from the end of the month, you wake early as usual and head straight to your bathroom. To your horror, you realise you're down to your last sheet of toilet paper. You hold it in, shower quickly and head to

work earlier than usual to relieve yourself in the staff bathroom, where there is a plentiful supply of paper. Inside the cubicle, you realise the cleaners have left a stash of brand new rolls on a windowsill.

You've never been one to raid office stationery, have always condemned it as stealing. But if you leave the toilet rolls where they are, you know you face another four mornings of drip-drying and bowel cramps.

So, do you bag the bog rolls or walk away?

TOILET TRIVIA

In 1977, somebody at the nuclear reactor at the University of Florida made the unfortunate mistake of flushing a toilet. The cooling system for the small, experimental reactor was tied into the city water main via the toilet. A sign above the toilet said, 'Please don't flush the toilet while the reactor is running'. However, untimely flushes caused the reactor to be shut down five times in three years.

In the mid 1960s, the Indonesian rupiah was valued at 325 to the dollar. The cheap paper that was used to print one-sen notes (worth 1/100th of a rupiah) was perfect for being used as toilet paper, and was much less expensive than the commercially made tissue paper, since you could get 32,500 pieces for a dollar.

It takes 13,000 gallons of water to carry away a mere 165 gallons of body waste per person each year.

SIT AND PONDER

Why do sleeping pills have warning labels that state: 'Caution – May Cause Drowsiness'?

Why are there flotation devices under plane seats instead of parachutes?

Why is it that when you are sleeping it's called drool but when you are awake it's called spit?

If you dig a hole in the South Pole are you digging up or down?

Why aren't there ever any guilty bystanders?

Why do fat chance and slim chance mean the same thing?

Why do mattresses have designs on them when they're always covered with sheets?

How come toy hippos are always blue or purple when real hippos are brown/grey?

The label on a package says 'Open here'. What is the protocol if the package says, 'Open somewhere else'?

Where are the germs that cause 'good' breath?

SIT AND LEARN

Here are 100 national flags for you to learn.
Don't forget to wash your hands afterwards:

 USA

Canada

European Union

Brazil

Bahrain

South Korea

North Korea

Italy

 Algeria

Australia

Madagascar

Chile

Venezuela

South Africa

United Kingdom

Albania

Bahamas

Pakistan

Marshall Islands

Vietnam

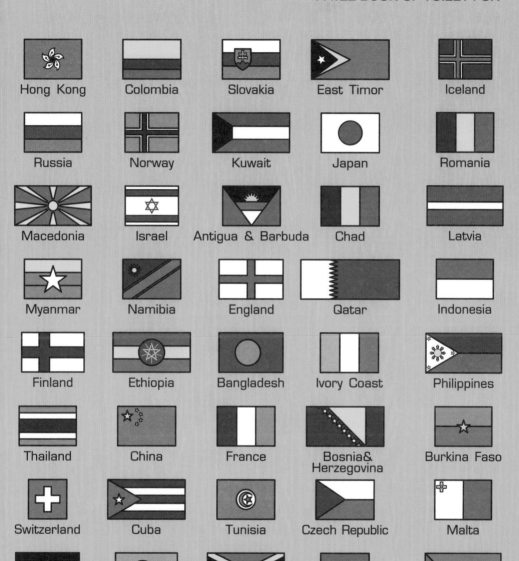

Hong Kong	Colombia	Slovakia	East Timor	Iceland
Russia	Norway	Kuwait	Japan	Romania
Macedonia	Israel	Antigua & Barbuda	Chad	Latvia
Myanmar	Namibia	England	Qatar	Indonesia
Finland	Ethiopia	Bangladesh	Ivory Coast	Philippines
Thailand	China	France	Bosnia& Herzegovina	Burkina Faso
Switzerland	Cuba	Tunisia	Czech Republic	Malta
Germany	Palau	Jamaica	Monaco	Sao Tome & Principe

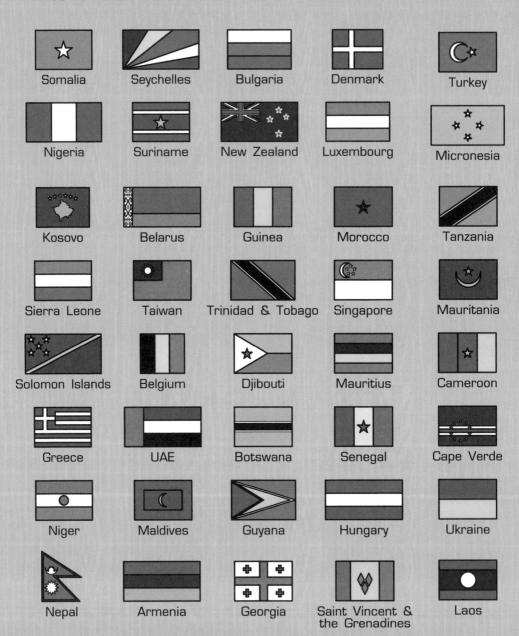

Somalia

Seychelles

Bulgaria

Denmark

Turkey

Nigeria

Suriname

New Zealand

Luxembourg

Micronesia

Kosovo

Belarus

Guinea

Morocco

Tanzania

Sierra Leone

Taiwan

Trinidad & Tobago

Singapore

Mauritania

Solomon Islands

Belgium

Djibouti

Mauritius

Cameroon

Greece

UAE

Botswana

Senegal

Cape Verde

Niger

Maldives

Guyana

Hungary

Ukraine

Nepal

Armenia

Georgia

Saint Vincent &
the Grenadines

Laos

TOILET PAPER HEIST

You are sitting on the toilet and suddenly realize that there is no paper. Someone has stolen it. You know four things:

1. There are only three possible culprits, your three puppies: Douglas, Cookie and Fergal.

2. Fergal never steals without Douglas's involvement.

3. Cookie can't open doors.

4. You had left the bathroom door closed.

Was Douglas involved?

TOILET TRIVIA

The 1960 film 'Psycho' was the first to show a toilet flushing. The scene prompted hundreds of complaints about indecency.

Hermann Göring eschewed regulation toilet paper. Only soft white handkerchiefs were good enough for the backside of the Commander-in-chief of the Luftwaffe.

The word 'loo' originates from the practice of emptying chamber pots out of the windows into the street, before the introduction of sewers. The French would shout 'gardez l'eau' (watch out for the water) to warn people below, but this became corrupted to 'gardy-loo' by the English.

If you want to find the cleanest toilet in a public convenience, the first toilet cubicle in a row is the least used and consequently the cleanest.

MAGIC SQUARE

Fill in all the blank cells to form a magic square in which each column, row and diagonal adds up to the same number.

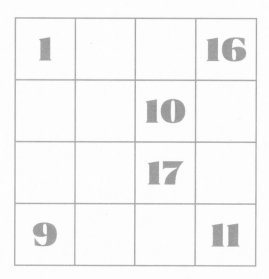

IS YOUR
TOILET PAPER
TRYING TO TELL YOU SOMETHING?

In days gone by, coy lovers communicated their passions in code, using a secret language of fans or flowers to make known their true feelings. These days, flirting in code is a dying art. Try spicing up your love life by leaving sweet-scented encoded expressions of love in the smallest room.

If the object of your desires is repeatedly fixing the toilet roll so that the paper hangs taut and out of reach, against the wall, you may as well forget it. S/he doesn't want you. It's never going to happen. Take your quilted comfort paper and move on.

This is more like it. Available, logical and neat, this is the work of someone who's interested, the toilet paper equivalent of meeting your gaze across a crowded bar. Game on.

You must really have messed up. This is the classic finger flip. You're loathed, despised, dumped. Bad luck, buddy.

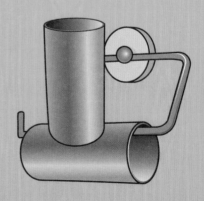

This one's a closed book. Unreadable, untouchable, remote and mysterious, this one's an island who is never going to bring you comfort.

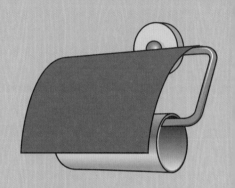

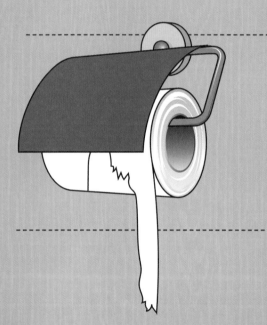

Tread carefully. This says 'available but damaged, unpredictable and potentially risky'. You can dive right in if you're game, but be prepared to be left with a mess on your hands.

If a life of chaos and indolence is what floats your boat, you're in luck. This is someone who sees no need to keep themselves or their house in order to welcome a lover.

Well, hello there, beautiful . . .
Now you're just flirting with me.

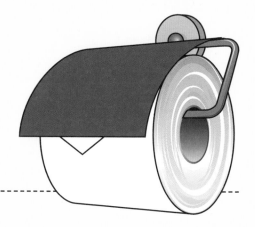

Inventive, fearless, experimental,
open-minded and playful. You're in
for quite a ride, just don't expect
commitment, 'cos that's not
what's on offer here.

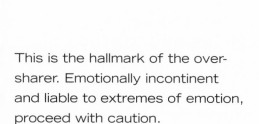

This is the hallmark of the over-
sharer. Emotionally incontinent
and liable to extremes of emotion,
proceed with caution.

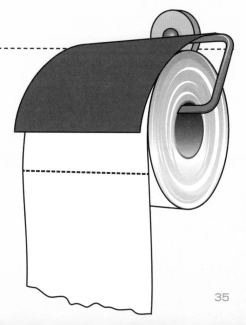

TWELVE TOILETS

How can you fit twelve toilets into nine cubicles, one per cubicle?

WHAT IS MISSING?

What is it about this paragraph that is so unusual? At first, it looks totally normal, but it isn't! Focusing your curious mind will bring its odd quality to light. A hint might assist you at this point; a common thing is missing! Still can't spot it? Go back and look again.

TOILET TRIVIA

More than 75 per cent of people admit to using their mobile phones and tablets on the toilet. Checking emails, texting, surfing the web and shopping on the loo have overtaken reading as the most popular activity.

SEND

COIN IN A WINE GLASS

Move two sticks so that the coin is
outside the wine glass.

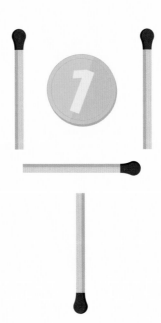

T☉ILET TIP

Three men in an exclusive hotel go to the toilet. They each tip the toilet attendant £5. The attendant feels guilty about taking so much of their money for just standing there while they use the facilities, so he gives five pound coins to his son and tells him to return the money to the gentlemen.

But the son keeps £2 for himself and only gives £3 back to the three men, £1 each, so they have effectively paid £4 each or £12 between them.

So if each of the gentlemen paid £4, the total paid is £12. Add the £2 in the son's pocket and this comes to £14.

What happened to the other £1?

HOW PAMPERED IS
YOUR BEHIND?

Do you give your backside the precise amount of respect and nurturing it deserves or do you neglect your old brown windsor? Do you place your chuff on a pedestal or do you treat it as an equal? Either way, it's wise to remember the old saying:
'You can lead a barking spider to water, but you can't turn it into a silk purse.'
How you approach your mustard road reveals a lot about your personality, your lifestyle and aspirations.
Answer these five questions to find out.

----

1. An eccentric millionaire offers you a lifetime supply of toilet paper. What is the minimum level of quilted softness you would tolerate in return for never again having to pay to wipe your lincoln tunnel?

A. Woodchip wallpaper with flecks of broken glass.
B. Baking parchment.
C. One-ply tissue.
D. Nothing less than three-ply quilted cashmere, enriched with extracts of Aloe Vera.

2. How do you feel about bidets?

A. Just thinking about that poncey French porcelain makes me hard Brexit.
B. I tried one once but I've never told anybody.
C. I can take them or leave them. I would have a go for a laugh in a hotel.
D. I love them. They are an essential part of my cleansing routine.

----

3. How low can your stash of toilet paper go without causing anxiety?

A. Who cares? When it runs out, there's always the shower curtain.
B. I need at least two stacked up to keep the collywobbles at bay.
C. I keep a spare roll hidden from the rest of the household.
D. There's always an unopened nine-pack in the bathroom.

----

4. Have you ever considered having your spadger bleached?

A. What? That's a thing? [facepalm]
B. No, and I wouldn't go there even if I won a gallon of
   hydroquinone in a church raffle.
C. No way. It wouldn't benefit or impress anyone in my life, least of all me.
D. Once a month. My crack is so white it glows in the dark.

----

5. If you could swap your backside for a celebrity behind, whose would you choose?

A. No one. My booty may not be perfect, but it's home-grown and one
   hundred per cent mine.
B. You're kidding right? I have a life.
C. Khloe Kardashian
D. Kim Kardashian

THE RESULTS

MOSTLY As:

You're a Grade A masochist who takes ownership of your golden rivet and you wear the pants in the relationship. You treat your kazoo very firmly as the workman's entrance – and it knows its place as a no frills conduit of brawny chuds. You are the supreme commander of your muddy third eye but you probably suffer from a neglected crop of hanging chalfonts.

MOSTLY Bs:

Your chocolate starfish is a shrinking violet. You would compromise comfort for a life on the cheapskate but that might be connected to your primal fear of running out of toilet tissue. You have a sturdy resistance to any form of back door beautification, so you do not seek perfection in the downstairs area. Function always trumps aesthetics.

MOSTLY Cs:

You won't compromise too far on comfort, but your secrecy betrays deep-seated trust issues as the self-appointed custodian of the concealed emergency roll. However, you would readily swap your modest buns for notable badonkadonk. Here lies the conflict: you wouldn't bleach for anyone but you would pump it up. This paradox is one of the aching nubs of the human condition.

MOSTLY Ds:

You're a hothouse flower. You're a French aristocrat. Your backside is so poodlized it could compete at Crufts. What's happened in your life that you devote so much of your meagre neural activity to your hind quarters? It's high time you learned that having a gleaming fragrant ring is no substitute for high self-esteem. So take your head out of your rusty sheriff's badge and get some professional therapy.

MAKE A KILLER PHANTOM LOG

YOU WILL NEED:

Hydrogen peroxide
Active dry yeast
Brown food colouring
Liquid soap
Large clean empty fizzy drink bottle
(at least one litre size)

1. Put three tablespoons of warm tap water into a cup and stir in two teaspoons of active dry yeast until it dissolves.

----

2. Pour half a cup of hydrogen peroxide into the bottle.

----

3. Add several drops of brown food colouring.

----

4. Add a tablespoon of liquid soap to the bottle and gently mix with the hydrogen peroxide by swirling it gently.

----

5. Place two metres of toilet paper in the bowl so that it sits on top of the water.

----

6. Pour the yeast solution into the bottle.

----

7. The yeast will release the oxygen in the hydrogen peroxide which will make the mixture grow in volume until it starts to pour out of the neck of the bottle.

8. Hold the bottle over the toilet bowl and allow the big brown trout to swirl onto the toilet paper until it fills the bowl.

----

9. Retreat to a safe distance and wait for the screams.

OUROBOROS

Fill every blank square with a letter by answering all of the clues given below. The direction of each word is indicated by an arrow on its initial letter.

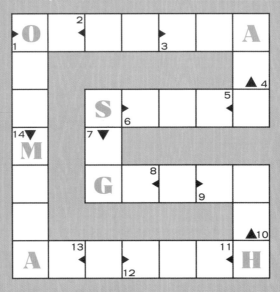

CLUES:

1. Hydrated amorphous form of silica (4)
2. Unit of length equal to 5 1/2 yards (4)
3. Towards or situated to the rear (5)
4. Secret political clique (5)
5. Soft flat hat (3)
6. Fill a suitcase (4)
7. Archaic exclamation (4)
8. A distinct period of history (3)
9. Scottish lake (4)
10. At low temperature (4)
11. Loose one-piece garment worn by ancient Romans (4)
12. East Germanic people that helped bring about the fall of the Western Roman Empire (4)
13. Sugar or syrup heated until it turns brown (7)
14. Latin American percussion instrument (6)

TAO OF THE TOILET – WHEN YOU FACE

STIFF OBSTACLES

My body is free of resistance and open to exciting new possibilities.

I think, act and eliminate like a boss.

Opportunities and advantages come every time I pull down my pants.

I believe in all the good things that are coming.

A river of compassion washes away my obstacles and replaces them with clarity.

I have as much shining gold to offer the world as the next person.

Wonderful things unfold beneath me.

I take comfort from the fact that I can leave this situation.

I choose to participate fully in this moment.

I believe in my ability to change the atmosphere with the business that I do.

TOILET TRIVIA

More people in the world have mobile phones than toilets. According to a United Nations report, more than 2.5 billion people on the planet do not have access to a toilet.

Taiwan is home to 'Modern Toilet', a chain of toilet-themed restaurants that serves food in miniature toilets and bathtubs to customers who sit on toilets while they eat. Drinks are served in urine collection bottles. Owner Wang Tzi-Wei is an ex banker who developed the chain after the success of his shop that specialised in poo-shaped ice cream served in mini toilets.

The World Toilet Organization – a global non-profit organization committed to improving toilet and sanitation conditions worldwide – was founded on 19th November 2001 and on this day every year World Toilet Day is celebrated.

DEATH SENTENCE

A serial killer is sentenced to death. He is allowed to make a final statement before his execution. If his statement is false he will be given the electric chair, but if his statement is true, he will be given a lethal injection. The condemned man makes his final statement and is released.
What did he say?

GROW STALACTITES AND
STALAGMITES
IN THE BATHROOM

YOU WILL NEED:

Two identical glasses
Epsom salts (Magnesium sulphate –
often called bath salts)
Tray
String/wool

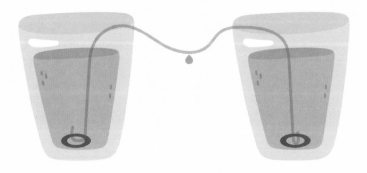

1. Fill the two glasses with water right up to their lips and then empty the water into a saucepan.

----

2. Heat the water on the stove and stir in teaspoon after teaspoon of Epsom salts. Keep the water very hot but don't let it boil.

----

3. Continue adding the bath salts until you can't dissolve any more.

----

4. Take the saucepan off the heat and allow the solution to cool for a few minutes until it can be poured into the glasses without cracking them.

----

5. Place the two glasses a foot apart on a tray on the bathroom windowsill and fill them with the solution.

6. Cut a piece of string or wool so that it is long enough to stretch from the bottom of one glass to the bottom of the other glass, leaving a dip in the middle.

----

7. Tie a metal washer onto each end of the string and place a washer in each glass.

----

8. If water drips off the string too quickly, you will just get a pool of water, so move the glasses further apart. If the string dries out, move the glasses closer together.

----

9. Over the next few days stalactites will form on the string and stalagmites will form on the tray beneath it.

SIT AND LEARN
APOSTROPHES

Many adults have never learned how to use apostrophes, but it is child's play if you follow these ten simple rules.

RULE 1:

Use the apostrophe with **CONTRACTIONS**.
Always place the apostrophe where the letter has been removed.

is not	isn't
do not	don't
He is over there.	He's over there.

RULE 2:

Use the apostrophe to show **POSSESSION**, that something belongs to someone.

the man's suitcase
the woman's bank account
the dog's bone
the actress's wig
Dr. Seuss's books

Note: Although names ending in S or an S sound do not require the second S in possessive, most people prefer to use it.

RULE 3:

Use the apostrophe when the noun that follows is IMPLIED.

This is my dog's, not your, dinner.

RULE 4:

When using PLURAL POSSESSION, make the plural first and then make the possession and place the apostrophe after it.

three lorries' engines

the Smiths' new car

I can remember ten people's names

RULE 5:

Don't use the apostrophe for the plural of a name.

They mentioned the Richardsons in the newspaper.

The Williamses hated our gift.

RULE 6:

If two or more people POSSESS THE SAME THING, only use apostrophe S after the second person.

Mum and dad's birthday

James and Martha's wedding.

RULE 7:

Never use an apostrophe with possessive pronouns: his, hers, its, theirs, ours, yours, whose.

> This wallet is hers.
>
> That dog has food in its bowl.
>
> Whose bowl is this? I don't care whose it is.

RULE 8:

The ONLY times 'it's' is used is for a CONTRACTION of 'it is' or 'it has'.

> It's sunny today.
>
> It's been raining.

RULE 9:

The plurals for capitals or numbers used as nouns do not use apostrophes.

We have test driven three SUVs.	[not SUV's]
It happened during the 1970s.	[not 1970's]
It happened during the '70s or mid-'70s	[not '70's or mid-'70's]

RULE 10:

The apostrophe goes after the thing doing the possessing.

The sun's rays	(the rays of the sun)
The dog's bones	(the bones of the dog)
The dogs' bones	(the bones of the dogs)
One month's rain	(the rain of one month)
Two months' rain	(the rain of two months)
Everyone's help	(the help of everyone)

FINALLY...

... there is much confusion about whether phrases such as 'girls school', 'Fathers Day', 'visitors book' and 'workers canteen' should include apostrophes. In most cases, there's no possession involved, so strictly, there should be no apostrophe.

girls school: a school for girls, not owned by girls
visitors book: a book for visitors, not owned by visitors
workers canteen: a canteen for workers, not owned by them

TOILET PAPER ALLOCATION

Three students share a house and they all have very different toilet paper requirements. Mike is responsible for about half of all the toilet paper consumed in the house, Jane uses a third but Allison only uses a mere one ninth. The remaining 6.6 per cent of the toilet paper is unaccounted for, but Allison and Jane suspect that Mike probably uses that too. Anyway, putting household tensions aside for a moment, Jane comes home from the supermarket with a packet of 17 toilet rolls. But they can't figure out how to divide up the toilet rolls so that everyone gets what they need, without splitting up a roll. Suddenly Allison has a brainwave. She borrows something from their next-door neighbour for five minutes that solves their dilemma. What does she borrow and why?

A FEW DAYS LATER . . .

Mike has made a considerable dent in his stash of toilet paper. Allison, Jane and their friend Susan have a good laugh speculating about how much he's squandered. Susan says, 'He must have at least one left, surely?'. In his defence, Allison says, 'He's got at least four toilet rolls left' to which Jane replies 'No, he definitely has fewer than four'. If only one of them is correct, how many rolls of toilet paper does Mike have left?

MAKE A
BIRD FEEDER

If you want to attract birds to your garden and help the bird population, especially during the winter when food is scarce, make a feeder. There are two options here. The first is so easy a five-year-old could do it. The second requires a little more skill and patience.

BASIC BIRD FEEDER

YOU WILL NEED:

A toilet roll
Peanut butter
Dinner plate
Bird seed
String

YOU WILL NEED:

A toilet roll
Paper plate
Hole punch
String
Scissors
Bird seed

DELUXE BIRD FEEDER

BASIC BIRD FEEDER

1. Smear the outside of a toilet paper tube with peanut butter. If you thought that feeding birds was its own reward, smearing on the peanut butter is probably one of the most satisfying things you will do today. Make sure you work it right up to the edges.

----

2. Pour birdseed on a dinner plate and then roll the toilet paper tube back and forward on the seeds until it is evenly coated.

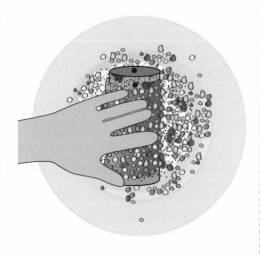

----

3. Poke the tube over a tree branch, or tie it to a branch with a piece of string.

DELUXE BIRD FEEDER

1. Cut two small semi-circles out of the bottom of one end of the toilet roll tube and then glue that end to the middle of a paper plate.

----

2. Punch three evenly spaced holes around the edge of the paper plate.

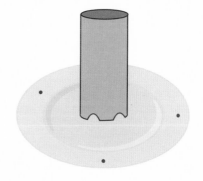

----

3. Cut three pieces of string each 25cm (10 in) long and tie them together at one end.

----

4. Thread each of the other ends through a hole in the paper plate and tie a knot to secure each one in place.

----

5. Fill the toilet roll with birdseed and then hang the feeder from a tree branch.

TOILET TRIVIA

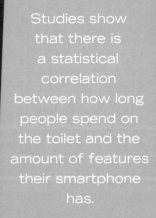

One third of people flush the loo while they are still sitting on it. You can save 2,190 gallons of water per person per year by only flushing the toilet once a day.

Germs from a flushing toilet can quickly spread through the air and cause infection, so once you have flushed, don't hang around. The germs can become airlifted in micro particles of water and cause infection. Smells are the same – if you can smell something bad, it means your nose is sampling a miniscule part of the offending matter.

Studies show that there is a statistical correlation between how long people spend on the toilet and the amount of features their smartphone has.

TIME TO PHONE THE
PLUMBER

The hapless house sharers Mike, Allison and Jane have another toilet-based dilemma. It's leaking but they are reluctant to spend the money on calling out an emergency plumber, especially since the leak appears to be quite small. So they agree that they will only call a plumber when half the bathroom floor has been flooded. Unfortunately, the leak gets worse and the floor area covered in water doubles every day. After twelve days the entire floor is covered in water. On which day should they have called the plumber, based on the original agreement?

ONE SQUARE

FOUR TRIANGLES

Move six sticks to leave one triangle
and three squares.

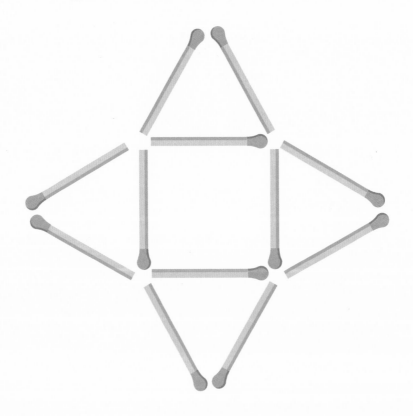

TAO OF THE TOILET
DIARRHOEA RELIEF

Effluent flows freely and abundantly through my life.

Sometimes you need to do what's best for you, not what's best for everyone else.

You might not be where you intended, but you've ended up where you needed to be.

I am grateful for the abundance that is flowing out of me.

I deserve whatever good passes through me today.

Be patient. Everything is slowly coming together.

I am open to accepting all forms of abundance the universe has to offer me.

My business is growing, expanding and thriving.

This morning I am brimming with purpose and overflowing with tangy butt nuts.

The more I give to the world, the more I get.

I welcome with open hands all that comes.

Things are always working out of me.

OUROBOROS

Fill every blank square with a letter by answering all of the clues given below. The direction of each word is indicated by an arrow on its initial letter.

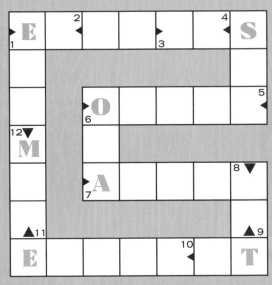

CLUES:

1. Always (4)
2. One of four collections which form the earliest body of Indian scripture (4)
3. A legal action (4)
4. Unit of land area equal to 4,840 square yards (4)
5. Wealthy, powerful person in business (6)
6. Female germ cell involved in reproduction (6)
7. In the Abrahamic religions, he was the first human (4)
8. Various branches of creative activity (4)
9. Ninth month of the Muslim year (7)
10. Angry (5)
11. Wanderer (5)
12. One who believes that the performance of economies are determined almost completely by changes in the money supply (10)

FOUR CANDLES

Here are four candles of different heights.
If they were all lit and sealed inside a glass tank containing air, which candle would go out first?

HINTS:

A candle flame consumes oxygen and produces water vapour and carbon dioxide.
Carbon dioxide is heavier than air.
There is one more thing you must factor in to make your decision.

BARNIE THE BEAR DESPERATELY NEEDS TO

PINCH ONE OFF

CAN YOU HELP HIM FIND HIS WAY TO THE BATHROOM BEFORE HE TOUCHES CLOTH?

WORD FILL

Find a four-letter word that turns each pair into
two nine-letter words:

1. PLACE _ _ _ _ START

2. WASTE _ _ _ _ SLIDE

3. AFTER _ _ _ _ GUARD

4. FLOOD _ _ _ _ CRASH

5. SUPER _ _ _ _ TRACK

6. FLASH _ _ _ _ SHADE

7. STERN _ _ _ _ CODES

8. WORKS _ _ _ _ MAKER

9. UNDER _ _ _ _ LIGHT

10. PITCH _ _ _ _ BALLS

11. MULTI _ _ _ _ HORSE

12. WRIST _ _ _ _ STAND

13. SHORT _ _ _ _ WATCH

14. BREAK _ _ _ _ BACKS

15. GUILD _ _ _ _ MARKS

16. WHIPS _ _ _ _ GRASS

17. SHORE _ _ _ _ TABLE

18. LATHE _ _ _ _ WORMS

19. MICRO _ _ _ _ BOARD

20. COVER _ _ _ _ KNOTS

SIT AND LEARN

Here are 190 countries and their capital cities for you to learn. Don't forget to wash your hands afterwards:

1. Abu Dhabi................. United Arab Emirates
2. Abuja....................... Nigeria
3. Addis Ababa .... Ethiopia
4. Algiers .... Algeria
5. Amman .... Jordan
6. Ankara...................... Turkey
7. Antananarivo .... Madagascar
8. Ashgabat.................. Turkmenistan
9. Asmara..................... Eritrea
10. Astana...................... Kazakhstan
11. Asuncion................... Paraguay
12. Athens...................... Greece
13. Bandar Seri Begawan. Brunei
14. Baghdad.......... Iraq
15. Bamako........... Mali
16. Bangkok.......... Thailand
17. Bangui............. Central African .... Republic
18. Banjul............. Gambia
19. Basseterre ...... Saint Kitts and Nevis
20. Beijing .... China
21. Beirut .... Lebanon
22. Belgrade.......... Serbia
23. Belmopan .... Belize
24. Berlin.............. Germany
25. Bern .... Switzerland

26.	Bishkek	Kyrgyzstan	43.	Cayenne	French Guiana
27.	Bissau	Guinea-Bissau	44.	Chisinau...........	Moldova
28.	Bogota	Colombia	45.	Colombo	Sri Lanka
29.	Brasilia	Brazil	46.	Conakry	Guinea
30.	Bratislava	Slovakia	47.	Copenhagen	Denmark
31.	Brazzaville	Congo, Republic of the	48.	Dakar	Senegal
			49.	Damascus	Syria
32.	Bridgetown	Barbados	50.	Dhaka.............	Bangladesh
33.	Brussels	Belgium	51.	Dar es Salaam..	Tanzania
34.	Budapest	Hungary	52.	Dili	East Timor
35.	Bucharest........	Romania	53.	Djibouti	Djibouti
36.	Buenos Aires ...	Argentina	54.	Doha	Qatar
37.	Bujumbura.......	Burundi	55.	Dublin	Ireland
38.	Cairo	Egypt	56.	Dushanbe	Tajikistan
39.	Canberra	Australia	57.	Edinburgh	Scotland
40.	Caracas...........	Venezuela	58.	Freetown	Sierra Leone
41.	Cardiff	Wales	59.	Gaborone	Botswana
42.	Castries...........	Saint Lucia			

THINGS TO DO ON THE LOO

60. Georgetown ..... Guyana
61. Guatemala City . Guatemala
62. Hanoi .... Vietnam
63. Harare .... Zimbabwe
64. Havana .... Cuba
65. Helsinki .... Finland
66. Honiara .... Solomon Islands
67. Islamabad .... Pakistan
68. Jakarta .... Indonesia
69. Juba .... South Sudan
70. Kabul .... Afghanistan
71. Kathmandu ...... Nepal
72. Khartoum .... Sudan
73. Kiev .... Ukraine
74. Kigali .... Rwanda
75. Kingston .... Jamaica
76. Kingstown .... Saint Vincent / Grenadines
77. Kinshasa .... Congo, Democratic Republic of the
78. Kuala Lumpur .. Malaysia
79. Kuwait City ...... Kuwait
80. La Paz .... Bolivia
81. Libreville .... Gabon
82. Lilongwe .... Malawi

83. Lima .... Peru
84. Lisbon .... Portugal
85. Ljubljana .... Slovenia
86. Lome .... Togo
87. London .... England
88. London .... United Kingdom
89. Luanda .... Angola
90. Lusaka .... Zambia
91. Luxembourg .... Luxembourg
92. Madrid .... Spain
93. Majuro .... Marshall Islands
94. Malabo .... Equatorial Guinea
95. Male .... Maldives
96. Managua .... Nicaragua
97. Manama .... Bahrain
98. Manila .... Philippines

99. Maputo .... Mozambique

100. Maseru .... Lesotho

101. Mbabana .... Swaziland

102. Melekeok .... Palau

103. Mexico City ...... Mexico

104. Minsk .... Belarus

105. Mogadishu .... Somalia

106. Monaco .... Monaco

107. Monrovia .... Liberia

108. Montevideo ...... Uruguay

109. Moroni .... Comoros

110. Moscow .... Russia

111. Muscat .... Oman

112. Nairobi .... Kenya

113. Nassau .... Bahamas

114. N'Djamena .... Chad

115. New Delhi .... India

116. Niamey .... Niger

117. Nicosia .... Cyprus

118. Nouakchott ..... Mauritania

119. Nuku'alofa .... Tonga

120. Ouagadougou .. Burkina Faso

121. Oslo .... Norway

122. Ottawa .... Canada

123. Palikir .... Federated States of Micronesia

124. Panama City .... Panama

125. Paramaribo ...... Suriname

126. Paris .... France

127. Phnom Penh .... Cambodia

128. Podgorica .... Montenegro

129. Port au Prince . Haiti

130. Port Louis .... Mauritius

131. Port Moresby ... Papua New Guinea

132. Port of Spain ... Trinidad and Tobago

133. Port Vila .... Vanuatu

134. Prague .... Czech Republic

THINGS TO DO ON THE LOO

158. Sofia .... Bulgaria

159. Stockholm .... Sweden

160. Suva................ Fiji

161. Taipei................ Taiwan

162. Tallinn .... Estonia

163. Tashkent .... Uzbekistan

164. Tbilisi .... Georgia

165. Tegucigalpa ...... Honduras

166. Tehran.............. Iran

167. Tel Aviv............. Israel

168. Amsterdam....... Netherlands

169. Thimphu .... Bhutan

170. Tirana (Tirane)... Albania

171. Tokyo .... Japan

172. Tripoli................ Libya

173. Tunis .... Tunisia

174. Ulaanbaatar...... Mongolia

175. Vaduz.............. Liechtenstein

176. Vaiaku .... Tuvalu

177. Valletta .... Malta

178. Vatican City ...... Vatican City

179. Victoria............. Seychelles

180. Vienna .... Austria

181. Vientiane .... Laos

182. Vilnius................. Lithuania

183. Warsaw .... Poland

184. Washington D.C. ... United States

185. Wellington .... New Zealand

186. Windhoek............. Namibia

187. Yamoussoukro...... Cote d'Ivoire

188. Yaounde .... Cameroon

189. Yerevan.............. Armenia

190. Zagreb .... Croatia

SIX
GLASSES

Line up six identical empty glasses. Fill the first three with water.

Now move only one glass so they alternate full, empty,
full, empty, full, empty.

THREE
TRIANGLES

Move two sticks to make four equilateral triangles.

ISLANDS IN THE
STREAM

Shade some squares so that each number is inside a white island with that given number of squares. The white islands may only touch diagonally, the black 'stream' must be continuous (i.e. no shaded squares cut off on their own) and shaded areas may not form or exceed 2 x 2 squares.

				7				
							6	
								9
		1				3		
2								
	4							
			3					

RED-EYED MONKS

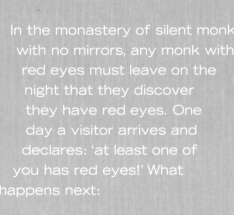

In the monastery of silent monks with no mirrors, any monk with red eyes must leave on the night that they discover they have red eyes. One day a visitor arrives and declares: 'at least one of you has red eyes!' What happens next:

a) if the visitor is telling the truth.

b) if the visitor is lying.

SIT AND PONDER

Why is it called 'after dark', when it's really after light?

If good things come to those who wait and all good things must come to an end, do some good things end before they have even come?

If every dog has his day, which ones have already had theirs? And do they know it? And if they do, what have they got left to live for?

If beggars can't be choosers, what happens if you choose to become a beggar and then immediately change your mind?

How do they get a deer to cross at that yellow road sign?

Why don't moths try to fly to the sun?

How come wrong numbers are never busy?

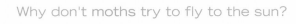

Do fish get thirsty?

How can you tell when it's time to tune your bagpipes?

Why do they make cars go so fast it's illegal?

TOILET TRIVIA

The suction toilet which was used in the International Space Station cost NASA $23.4 million to design and manufacture.

The recommended method of washing your hands after going to the toilet is rigorous washing with soap for at least 20 seconds. Only 5 per cent of people do this.

When leaving a public bathroom, you don't have to open the door with your sleeve because the handle or knob is one of the cleanest areas – germs can't survive in cool, dry places for very long.

PATH HUNTER

Draw a continuous line from one green dot to the other. You may move vertically or horizontally but NOT diagonally. Your line cannot pass through a red dot. The numbers tell you how many white or green dots your line passes through in that row or column.

THE PHANTOM LOGGER

Inside one of these bowls lurks a phantom log that won't go away, despite several flushes. The wily culprit has left four signs to alert those clever enough to decipher the clues.

1. It's in 2 or 3

2. It's in 1 or 4

3. It's in here

4. It's not in here

But only one of the warnings is correct.

Can you correctly locate the obstinate brown trout?

TAO OF THE TOILET – WHEN YOU FACE

STIFF OBSTACLES

Dear Universe, I am totally open to something awesome occurring.

The power is within me. I am a powerful creator.

I am peacefully allowing my colon to unfold.

I believe in my ability to manifest into physical reality whatever is inside me.

Weak desire brings weak results.

Today I make things happen.

I work hard in silence and let success be my noise.

I observe my movements without getting attached to them.

I am becoming a success magnet. Success sticks to me and cannot be washed away.

Success simply falls into my lap.

MAKE A
PØLLUTIØN
DETECTØR

How often have you joked about levels of radioactivity in the bathroom after you've paid a visit? But did you know that there is a lot more gunk floating around in the air than you think? Dust particles, minute flakes of skin, bacteria, pollen, faecal matter, you name it – if it's lighter than air, you're breathing it in. Here's how to catch a glimpse into the miniscule bathroom world that finds its way up your nose.

YOU WILL NEED:
Paper plate
String
Petroleum jelly
Hole punch
Black light (optional)

1. Use a hole punch to make a hole in a paper plate.

2. Thread a piece of string through the hole.

3. Smear petroleum jelly evenly over both sides of the plate.

4. Hang the plate from the ceiling and let it float around collecting pollution for at least a week.

5. If you own a microscope and want to take a closer look at what you've caught, scoop some of the petroleum jelly off the plate and smear it on a microscope slide.

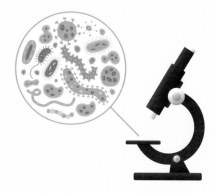

You'll be amazed at how much your little homemade pollution detector has collected in such a short time. Imagine what it would look like if you left it hanging for a whole year!

DID YOU KNOW?
Petroleum jelly contains phosphors so it glows bright blue under a black light and allows some particles to stand out more. The phosphors absorb radiation from the black light and emit it as visible blue light.

TOILET TRIVIA

One of the most expensive bathrooms in the world is located in the Kowloon shop of Hong Kong-based Hang Fung Gold Technology Ltd. The toilet is coated with gems and is 24-carat gold, along with the sink, tiles and doors. The suite was valued at US $29 million in 2010.

A toilet paper roll made from 22-carat gold went on sale in 2013. Sold by the Australian company Toilet Paper Man, it was priced at £825,000. It is delivered personally with a bottle of champagne. If that's too pricey but you still want to add an opulent sparkle to your business, 24-carat gold pills designed by late New York artist Tobi Wong cost a mere US $425 for three.

In 2013, Kim Kardashian and Kanye West reportedly splashed out £460,000 on four gold-plated loos for their Bel Air mansion.

SIT AND PONDER

WOULD YOU RATHER...

1. Be the Taekwondo world champion or have a real working lightsaber?

2. Be the only happy person on earth, or the only unhappy person on earth?

3. Be half your height or double your weight?

4. Live the rest of your life on an executive yacht or in a log cabin in the woods?

5. Die in peace or live an extra ten years and die in pain?

6. Have a prestigious university named after you or an iconic sports stadium named after you?

7. Never have to sleep or never have to eat?

8. Wake up with £100 in your pocket every morning or £300 hidden somewhere in your house, that takes you seven hours to find every day.

9. Relive your birth or watch your conception?

10. Have a beer belly or a double chin?

WALKING COMMUTER

Every day after work, Penny catches the train and is then picked up at the station by her partner, who drives her home. One evening Penny catches an earlier train and arrives at the station an hour earlier than normal, so she starts walking home. Penny's partner picks her up along the route and they get home ten minutes earlier than usual. Assuming that her partner always drives the entire journey at a constant speed, how long did Penny spend walking?

HITORI

Black out some of the cells in the grid so that
each row and each column contains no duplicated
numbers. Blacked out cells must not touch
horizontally or vertically and all white cells must form
one continuous area.

6	1	1	3	5	2
2	6	1	2	4	5
2	3	6	5	1	4
4	3	2	1	3	3
1	4	5	1	5	3
5	2	3	4	4	1

MAKE A TOILET
STINK
BOMB

The next time someone criticizes you
for stinking out the bathroom, show
them what a really foul odour smells like
by making your own stink bomb using half
a dozen eggs and some drain cleaner.

YOU WILL NEED:

Six eggs

Drano (or any other sodium hydroxide-based drain cleaner)

Jar with a lid

Protective goggles and rubber gloves

1. Crack six eggs and separate the yolks from the whites.

2. Put on rubber gloves and protective goggles and pour two tablespoons of Drano into an empty storage jar.

3. Add half a cup of water and then stir in the egg whites.

4. Screw the lid tightly onto the jar.

5. Keep the jar in a warm place for four or five days to allow the drain cleaner to rot the egg whites.

6. Wait until you get it in the neck for leaving an unpleasant odour, then place the jar on the bathroom windowsill and remove the lid.

STINK BOMB

7. Go and stay with a friend.

ANSWERS

PAGE 7
SLITHERLINK

	2		2		3	
2	2					2
3	2	2	2	3		2
2	2	3		1	0	1
1		1	1	1	0	1
0					1	1
	1		1		2	

PAGE 8
THREE TOILETS
She turns on Switches 1 and 2 and waits for three minutes. Then she turns off Switch 2 and goes to the ground floor toilet. If the light is on, she knows this is Switch 1. If the light is off, she should touch the bulb. If the bulb is still warm, it is operated by Switch 2; if it is cold, it's Switch 3. Next, she climbs the stairs to the first floor, where she uses the same logic to find the correct switch. The remaining switch must operate the bulb on the second floor.

PAGE 14
BATHROOM TILES
There are 30 rectangles.

PAGE 15
RIDDLE WHILE YOU PIDDLE
1. Pull the plug.
2. The match.

PAGE 16
URINAL CAKE
He makes two cuts perpendicular to each other along the diameter and then the third in cross section.

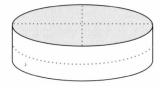

PAGE 18
DRUG DILEMMA
Break each pill in half and place them in two separate cups. Now you know that each cup contains half a pill A and half a pill B. Now take another pill from Bottle A, break it in half and add a half to each cup. Now each cup contains the correct dose: one pill A (in two halves) and half a pill B.

PAGE 19
THREE UTILITIES 3D PUZZLE
This classic puzzle has no solution in 2D. But if you place everything

ANSWERS

on a 3D doughnut shape, you can make the elusive ninth link by passing through the hole and coming round the other side.

PAGE 29
TOILET PAPER HEIST
Yes. Either Fergal or Douglas opened the door and Fergal never steals without Douglas.

PAGE 31
MAGIC SQUARE

1	13	7	16
15	8	10	4
12	2	17	6
9	14	3	11

PAGE 36
TWELVE TOILETS

PAGE 37
WHAT IS MISSING?
The letter 'e'

PAGE 38
COIN IN A WINE GLASS

PAGE 39
TOILET TIP
The three gentlemen ended up giving £12 between them, of which £10 stayed with the toilet attendant and the remaining £2 stayed with the son. There is no missing £1.

ANSWERS

PAGE 46
OUROBOROS

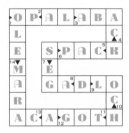

1. opal
2. pole
3. aback
4. cabal
5. cap
6. pack
7. egad
8. age
9. loch
10. cold
11. toga
12. Goth
13. caramel
14. maraca

PAGE 49
DEATH SENTENCE

He said 'I will die by electric chair' making it impossible for the sentence to be carried out. If the electric chair was used, his statement would have been true, and if he had been given a lethal injection, his statement would have been false.

PAGE 56
TOILET PAPER ALLOCATION

Allison borrowed an extra roll of toilet paper. It was easy to split up 18 rolls: 9 for Mike (half), 6 for Jane (one third) and just 2 for herself (one ninth). This left one roll spare, which she returned to their neighbour.

PAGE 57
A FEW DAYS LATER . . .

Allison can't be right because that would mean that Susan would also be right. If Susan's assertion is correct then so is either Allison or Jane. This means only Jane can be right: Mike has fewer than four toilet rolls left.

PAGE 61
TIME TO PHONE THE PLUMBER

On the twelfth day the entire floor was covered, so that must mean that half the floor was covered the day before. They should have called the plumber on the eleventh day.

PAGE 62
ONE SQUARE, FOUR TRIANGLES

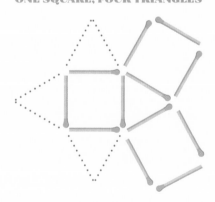

ANSWERS

PAGE 64
OUROBOROS

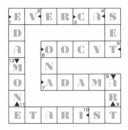

1. ever
2. Veda
3. case
4. acre
5. tycoon
6. oocyte
7. Adam
8. arts
9. Ramadan
10. irate
11. nomad
12. monetarist

PAGE 65
FOUR CANDLES

The tallest one goes out first because the carbon dioxide is hot so it rises to the top of the jar and deprives it of oxygen.

PAGE 66
BARNIE THE BEAR – MAZE

PAGE 67
WORD FILL

1. kick
2. land
3. life
4. gate
5. race
6. lamp
7. post
8. pace
9. foot
10. fork
11. pack
12. band
13. stop
14. fast
15. hall
16. tall
17. bird
18. ring
19. chip
20. slip

PAGE 74
SIX GLASSES

Pick up the second glass from the left and pour the contents into the fifth glass from the left and then put it back in place. You have only moved one glass.

ANSWERS

PAGE 74
THREE TRIANGLES

PAGE 75
ISLANDS IN THE STREAM

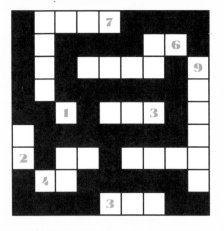

PAGE 76
RED-EYED MONKS

a) If there is only one red-eyed monk, he will look around and see that no one else has red eyes, so it must be him. So he will leave that night.

If there are two red-eyed monks, both of them will see a monk with a red eye, but in the morning when neither of them has left, they will realize that they too have red eyes. So they will both leave on the second night.

If there are three red-eyed monks, following the same logic, they will leave on the third night.

And so on.

b) Every monk will look around and see that no one else has red eyes and assume it must be him. So everyone will leave that night.

PAGE 79
PATH HUNTER

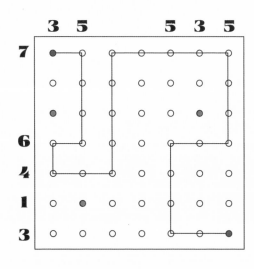

ANSWERS

PAGE 80
PHANTOM LOGGER

If the log is in Bowl 1, then both 2 and 4 are true. If the log is in Bowl 2, then both 1 and 4 are true. If the log is in Bowl 3, then 1, 3 and 4 are true. The log is in Bowl 4.

PAGE 86
WALKING COMMUTER

If they saved ten minutes, then Penny must have been a five-minute drive away from the station when she was picked up, because her partner saved having to drive the extra five minutes to the station and then back again. Therefore, Penny must have been walking for 50 minutes.

PAGE 87
HITORI

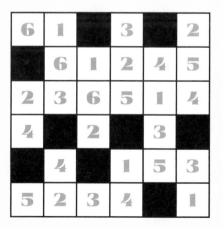

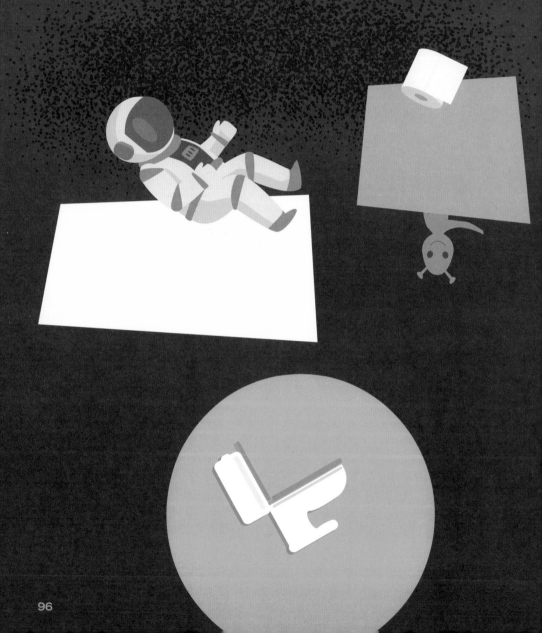